It's Crossword Time 2

Test Your Vocabulary

It's Crossword Time 2

Peter Watcyn-Jones

Illustrated by Colin Mier

PENGUIN ENGLISH

PENGUIN ENGLISH

Published by the Penguin Group
Penguin Books Ltd, 27 Wrights Lane, London W8 5TZ, England
Penguin Books USA Inc., 375 Hudson Street, New York, New York 10014, USA
Penguin Books Australia Ltd, Ringwood, Victoria, Australia
Penguin Books Canada Ltd, 10 Alcorn Avenue, Toronto, Ontario, Canada M4V 3B2
Penguin Books (NZ) Ltd, 182–190 Wairau Road, Auckland 10, New Zealand
Penguin Books Ltd, Registered Offices: Harmondsworth, Middlesex, England

Test Your Vocabulary: It's Crossword Time 2 published by Penguin Books 1992
10 9 8 7 6 5 4 3 2

Illustrations by Colin Mier
Designed by Karen Osborne

Filmset in Century Schoolbook

Printed and bound in Great Britain by
BPC Hazell Books Ltd
A member of
The British Printing Company Ltd

Contents

Opposites: adjectives

Complete the crossword by finding a word that is opposite in meaning to each of the adjectives. (See example)

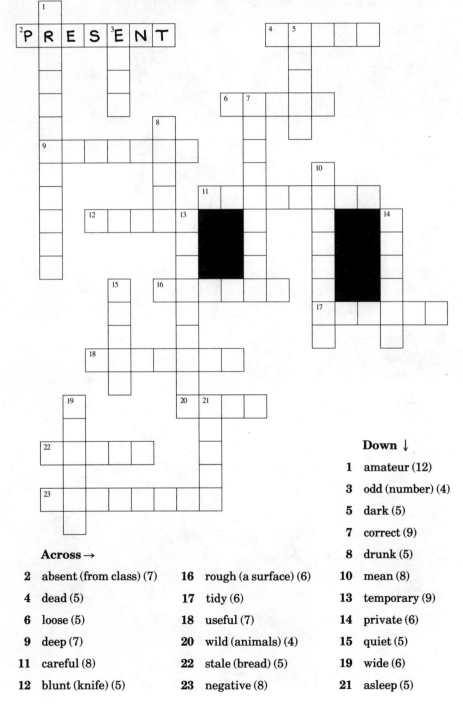

Down ↓

1 amateur (12)

3 odd (number) (4)

5 dark (5)

7 correct (9)

8 drunk (5)

10 mean (8)

13 temporary (9)

14 private (6)

15 quiet (5)

19 wide (6)

21 asleep (5)

Across →

2 absent (from class) (7)

4 dead (5)

6 loose (5)

9 deep (7)

11 careful (8)

12 blunt (knife) (5)

16 rough (a surface) (6)

17 tidy (6)

18 useful (7)

20 wild (animals) (4)

22 stale (bread) (5)

23 negative (8)

Picture crossword: fruit and vegetables

Look at the drawings and complete the crossword.

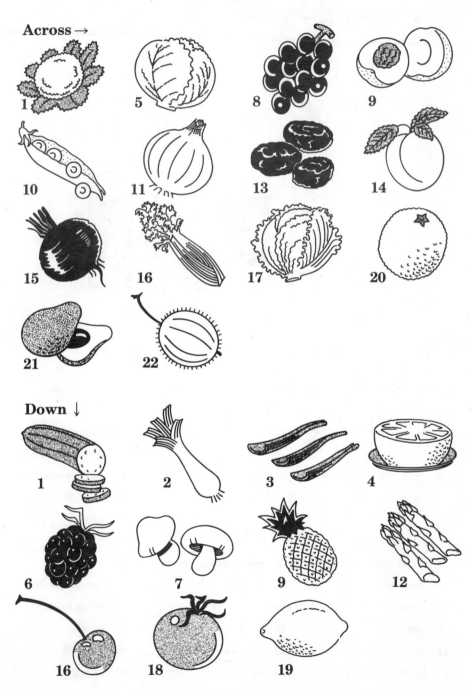

Across →

1 5 8 9

10 11 13 14

15 16 17 20

21 22

Down ↓

1 2 3 4

6 7 9 12

16 18 19

3 Complete the sentences

Complete the crossword by filling in the missing words in each of the sentences. (See example)

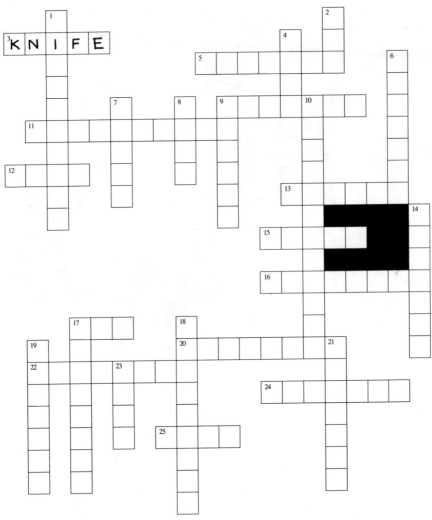

Across →

3 I can't cut this meat, my .... isn't sharp enough. (5)

5 In case you are not satisfied with something you have bought in a shop, remember to keep the .... (7)

9 According to the advertisement in the paper, the book costs £25, including .... and packing. (7)

11 Oh Pat, do you think you could get me some stamps from the ....? (4,6)

12 You'll have to speak louder, I'm afraid. Aunt Mary's a bit .... (4)

13 The job offered a .... of £18,000 a year. (6)

15 'Atishoo!'
'.................... you!' (5)

16 Pass me a pair of .... please, Brian. I want to cut this article out of the newspaper. (8)

17 I always wanted a .... as a child, but my parents didn't think there was room in our flat for a dog or a cat. (3)

20 It looks like rain. You'd better take an .... with you. (8)

22 The .... on the front page of the newspaper said: FIVE ARRESTED FOR BOMB DEATHS. (8)

24 I never buy books, I always borrow them from the local .... (7)

25 She asked for a room with a .... of the sea. (4)

Down ↓

1 'What does insolent mean?'
'I've no idea. Look it up in the ....' (10)

2 These shoes don't ....; they're too small. (3)

4 She weighed 10 kilos too much, so her doctor advised her to go on a .... (4)

6 We could tell someone was at home because there was smoke coming out of the .... (7)

7 In the last football match of the season Liverpool beat Manchester United by three .... to one. (5)

8 'Coffee, John?'
'Yes, please. Sugar but no ....' (4)

9 I usually fill my car up with .... on my way to work on Monday morning. (6)

10 Could you arrange the list of students in .... order, please? (12)

14 Could you read this for me please, David? I can't see a thing without my .... (7)

17 The train standing at .... 7 is the 14.25 to Swansea. (8)

18 The examiner asked her a lot of very difficult .... (9)

19 She went to the ....'s to get some medicine. (7)

21 My cousin is flying to Canada tomorrow, so we're all going to the .... to see him off. (7)

23 The .... was out of order, so we had to use the stairs to get to the seventh floor. (4)

4 Jobs and occupations

Put the mixed-up letters for each word in the right order to complete the crossword. Each word is a job or occupation. To help you, the answers are given in alphabetical order at the foot of the page. (See example)

Across →		Down ↓	
3	antiwrecaffrd (7,6)	1	arestisw (8)
4	hirtcacet (9)	2	retache (7)
7	octodr (6)	5	createprn (9)
9	sunre (5)	6	rolitaunsj (10)
12	tensdit (7)	8	muandts (7)
13	dasirerehsr (11)	10	sasnmeal (8)
16	mefrra (6)	11	rirbailna (9)
19	caesryert (9)	14	kerab (5)
20	enirm (5)	15	amisbsnsenu (11)
23	thurecb (7)	17	ltareeccini (11)
26	tve (3)	18	croat (5)
28	ltoip (5)	21	fceh (4)
29	staaneeettg (6,5)	22	pemaolcni (9)
30	apiconit (8)	24	himcncea (8)
		25	erarbb (6)
		27	satpnom (7)

actor   architect   baker   barber   businessman   butcher carpenter   chef   dentist   doctor   dustman   electrician estate agent   farmer   hairdresser   journalist   librarian   mechanic miner   nurse   optician   pilot   policeman   postman   salesman secretary   teacher   traffic warden   vet   waitress

Classifications

Complete the crossword by finding one word to classify each of the groups of three words. (See example)

Across →

1 Arabic, Swedish, Dutch (9)

5 bracelet, ring, earring (9)

6 theft, murder, fraud (6)

8 leek, cauliflower, cabbage (10)

9 10/12/44, 1/9/58, 21/2/91 (5)

12 knife, fork, spoon (7)

13 beech, oak, pine (5)

15 square, triangle, rectangle (6)

16 Africa, Asia, Europe (10)

17 grapes, pineapples, peaches (5)

18 van, car, lorry (8)

19 Jupiter, Mars, Venus (7)

20 crocodile, snake, lizard (8)

Down ↓

2 bull, goat, fox (7)

3 bridge, chess, dominoes (5)

4 copper, iron, tin (6)

7 kilos, pounds, grammes (7)

10 yen, pound sterling, lira (10)

11 dagger, gun, sword (7)

14 wasp, beetle, ant (7)

6 People 1

Read the sentences and complete the crossword. (See example)

Across →

3 Someone who takes something from a shop without paying for it. (10)

6 A person who represents his or her country abroad. (10)

10 Someone who eats fruit and vegetables, but never eats meat. (10)

13 A person who gets secret information from another country. (3)

15 A person who has deliberately killed someone. (8)

18 Someone who sees a person breaking the law. (7)

19 A person who draws plans for new buildings. (9)

20 A person who betrays his or her own country. (7)

Down ↓

1 Someone who steals. (5)

2 Someone who always looks for the best in life. (8)

4 Someone who has left his or her country for political reasons. (7)

5 Someone who rides a horse in a race. (6)

7 Someone who breaks into houses, shops, etc. in order to steal. (7)

8 Someone who is travelling on foot in a street. (10)

9 An unmarried man. (8)

11 Someone who visits another country or district for a holiday. (7)

12 Someone who writes music. (8)

14 Someone on the other side in a game or a contest. (8)

16 A shopkeeper who sells newspapers. (9)

17 Someone who watches a sport or an event without taking part himself or herself. (9)

7 Collective nouns

Complete the crossword by filling in the gaps in the story.

Mr Brown took out a ....(14 across) of writing paper and
began to make a list of things he wanted to buy. He had a lot of
shopping to do today and wanted to make sure he would
remember everything.

Half an hour later, Mr Brown left the house. As he was getting
the car out of the garage he noticed that a ....(5 down) of
glass on the garage door was missing. 'I must remember to fix
that some time,' he thought to himself.

When he reached town, the first shop he went into was W.H.
Smith's. He had three things he wanted to buy there – a
....................(11 down) of cards for his son, William, a
....................(12 across) of string and the local newspaper. Next
door to W.H. Smith's was Boots the chemist. He looked at his list.
Yes, there were some things he needed to get there. He went
inside and bought a ....(12 down) of soap, a ....
(6 across) of toothpaste and a ....(2 down) of shampoo.

Then he went upstairs to the camera department and bought a
....................(9 down) of film for his daughter, Heather.

The next place he wanted to go to was Tesco's – a large
supermarket. As he was walking along, he passed a furniture
shop. In the window was a very expensive ....(1 down) of
drawers. 'Good heavens! Who on earth can afford to buy that?' he
thought to himself.

Two minutes later he was inside Tesco's. He looked at his list.
'Right, let's see now … a ....(4 across) eggs, a
....................(13 down) of bread and a ....(5 across) of milk.'
Slowly, his trolley began to fill up. He checked his list again. 'A
....................(14 down) of apples and a ....(8 down) of jam.'
Fifteen minutes later, he was standing in the queue at the check-
out counter. As he was waiting he noticed a large sign which said:
THIS WEEK'S SPECIAL OFFER – TWO ....(8 across) OF
SOCKS – 90p! He decided to buy them.

There were only two more places left to go now – the
tobacconist's and the florist's. He was glad. The shopping bags
were very heavy.

At the tobacconist's he bought a ....(15 down) of
matches and a ....(11 across) of cigarettes. The shop also
sold sweets, so he decided to buy a ....(12 down) of
chocolate to eat later that evening when he watched television.

The florist's was at the end of the arcade and as he got near it he
noticed a ....(16 across) of people watching a young man
playing the guitar and singing. He had his guitar case open in
front of him and, as he passed, Mr Brown saw that there was a
....................(3 down) of money in it. Mr Brown liked music, so he
opened his wallet, took out a £5 ....(10 across) and
dropped it into the case.

At the florist's he bought a large ....(7 down) of daffodils
for his wife, Julia. As the assistant wrapped them up, he looked at
his watch. It was five o'clock. He would have to hurry if he wanted
to be home before his wife got back from work.

Picture crossword: animals

Look at the drawings and complete the crossword.

Across →

2 4 6 8

10 12 14 16

18 20 21 22

23 24

Down ↓

1 2 3 5

7 9 11 13

15 17 19 22

Opposites: verbs

Complete the crossword by finding a word that is opposite in meaning to each of the verbs.

Across →		Down ↓	
1	defend (6)	1	deny (5)
2	appear (9)	3	hide (4)
4	lower (5)	5	float (boat) (4)
6	lengthen (7)	6	fail (7)
7	loosen (7)	8	export (6)
10	destroy (6)	9	take one's time, dawdle (5)
11	accept (6)	13	encourage (10)
12	contract (metal) (6)	14	weaken (10)
14	save (money) (5)	17	punish (6)
15	arrive (6)		
16	forbid (5)		
18	remember (6)		
19	increase (8)		

Word association 1

Complete the crossword by finding out which word each of the groups of three words can be associated with. (See example)

Across →

4 surgeon, ward, ambulance (8)

6 bark, leash, poodle (3)

8 branch, trunk, beech (4)

10 books, borrow, reference (7)

12 daffodil, stem, petal (6)

13 carols, turkey, presents (9)

14 frame, canvas, watercolour (8)

17 crossbar, handlebars, saddle (7)

18 bonnet, overtake, Volvo (3)

19 bank, Thames, flow (5)

20 sleeve, collar, cuff (5)

22 umpire, serve, net (6)

Down ↓

1 corner, goal, kick-off (8)

2 beak, nest, pigeon (4)

3 telescope, galaxy, black hole (9)

5 sheet, pillow, blanket (3)

7 club, hole, green (4)

9 headline, circulation, reporter (9)

11 relay, Olympic Games, lap (9)

15 receiver, dial, directory (9)

16 playground, blackboard, homework (6)

21 best man, ring, bride (7)

In this crossword all the words have been filled in, but the clues are all mixed up. Write the correct answer (1 Down, 8 Across, etc.) in front of each clue. (See example)

26

3 Down

.... A person who pays to stay in someone else's house.

.... A type of fish.

.... A common illness (especially amongst children) where the glands swell, particularly the neck and mouth.

.... A religious festival in March or April when Christians remember the death of Jesus Christ and his return to life.

.... Unable to read or write.

.... Used to stick things together, e.g. wood, paper, etc.

.... The main part of a tree.

.... The yellow part of an egg.

.... To travel regularly a long distance between one's house and work.

.... Part of a car which you lift up to see the engine.

.... A natural disaster where a mass of snow and ice crashes down the side of a mountain.

.... A container for money.

.... To walk unsteadily, e.g. if you are ill or drunk.

.... One of the signs of the zodiac (someone born between June 23–July 23).

.... Being able to speak two languages fluently.

.... A common yellow spring flower.

.... To look quickly at something.

.... Very old.

.... Expecting a baby.

.... How some people feel when they look down from a high building.

.... To talk about other people, especially about their private lives.

.... A word that ends with the same sound as another, e.g. 'mouse', 'house'.

.... Having no money.

.... The line running from the front to the back of the head when hair is combed in opposite directions.

.... Your voice may sound like this if you have been speaking or shouting all day.

12 The dinner party

Complete the crossword by filling in the gaps in the story. To help you, the first letter of each missing word is given.

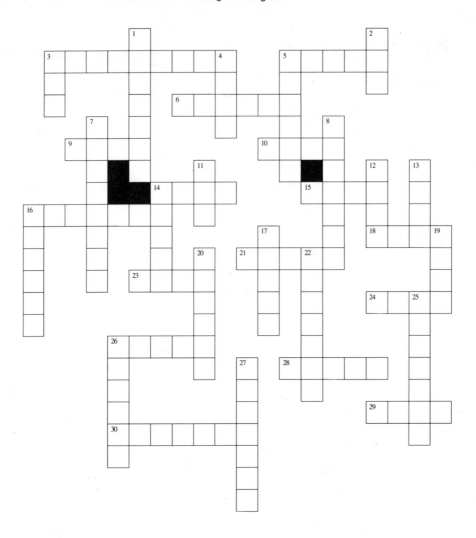

I don't know w...................(1 down) the following story is true or n...................
(3 down) but according to a friend of m...................(9 across) it happened to her
sister a c...................(16 down) of years ago.

My friend's sister w...................(5 down) for an advertising agency and one
particular evening had invited h...................(2 down) boss and several important
clients home for a m...................(10 across).

She wanted to m...................(15 across) a good impression and one of the things

she intended to make was a salmon mousse. She had just f...................(7 down)
cleaning the fish and left it on the kitchen table w...................(5 across) she
gathered up the r...................(29 across) of the ingredients. However, while her
back was turned her cat jumped o...................(23 across) the table and started
eating the fish. Fortunately, she h...................(28 across) it purring and quickly
chased it a...................(14 across). At the s...................(13 down) time she thought to
herself, 'Well, n...................(20 down) will know that the cat has nibbled the fish'.
Consequently, she washed and cleaned it a...................(14 down) and got on with
her preparations.

The dinner party was a great s...................(25 down) and as the guests left they
t...................(27 down) her very much and were especially complimentary about
the salmon mousse. As she was c...................(16 across) the gate after the last car
had left she suddenly n...................(22 down) her cat in the flower-bed near the
front door. It was very stiff and very dead!

'Oh, my God!' she thought. 'The fish. There m...................(19 down) have been
something wrong with it!'.

Feeling very worried, she rushed to the phone and c...................(26 down) all her
guests to e...................(30 across) and advise t...................(18 across) to visit the
doctor immediately. Of course, they were not particularly p...................(8 down) to
know that she had given them food that the cat had eaten. J...................(24 across)
as she had made the last phone call the doorbell rang. It was her next-door
n...................(3 across), looking very nervous. He explained that earlier that
evening he had unfortunately run over her c...................(11 down). He was very
s...................(17 down) but he had been in a great hurry at the time as he was on
his way to meet a train. He had r...................(4 down) the doorbell but
unfortunately c...................(26 across) not make anyone hear above the noise of the
d...................(6 across) party. Instead he had l...................(12 down) the cat by the
front door. Had she f...................(21 across) it yet?

(Adapted from *The Book of Nasty Legends* by Paul Smith, Routledge & Kegan Paul)

One word only

Complete the crossword by finding one word for the words in **bold type** in the sentences. (See example)

Across →

2   We have very nice **people living next-door**. That's one of the reasons we don't want to move from here. (10)

5   By the way, this is my **brother's daughter**, Samantha. (5)

8   The **men who ran the ship** all came from Pakistan. (4)

9   It was such a large department store that it took us quite a while to find the **way out**. (4)

11 She **said she was sorry** for the way she had behaved at the party. (10)

14 Most modern department stores have **moving staircases**. (10)

15 The **people sitting in the theatre** applauded loudly at the end of the performance. (8)

17 News has just come in of a severe **shortage of food** in Africa. (6)

18 Two men have been **caught by the police** in connection with the recent bank robberies in Brighton. (8)

20 He was a very bad tennis player when he started taking lessons, but **little by little** he got better and is now one of the best players in the club. (9)

Down ↓

1   Jeans usually **get smaller** the first time you wash them. (6)

3   I would find it very difficult to **leave my country and settle elsewhere**. (8)

4   We're off to Majorca for a **period of two weeks** in July. (9)

6   The police are still looking for the three prisoners who managed to **get free** from Parkhurst prison at the weekend. (6)

7   Although there were more than 300 **people applying for the job**, fewer than five per cent were suitably qualified. (10)

10 The student's work **got better** towards the end of the term. (8)

12 Have you **made up your mind** where you're going for your holidays this year? (7)

13 You don't have to do it – it's **entirely of your own free choice**. (9)

16 She was very stubborn and **turned down** all offers of help. (7)

19 We shall probably see a great many changes during the next **ten years**. (6)

14 EYE is to SEE as EAR is to HEAR

*Complete the crossword by filling in the missing words in the sentences.
(See example)*

DIRECTORY

32

Across →

2 DICTIONARY is to WORD as .... is to TELEPHONE NUMBER. (9)

5 ....is to HIVE as SPIDER is to WEB. (3)

6 STEM is to FLOWER as .... is to TREE. (5)

7 .... is to AUDIBLE as SEE is to VISIBLE. (4)

8 .... is to MEAT as GREENGROCER is to VEGETABLES. (7)

11 ....is to SHEEP as HERD is to CATTLE. (5)

12 .... are to LEOPARD as STRIPES are to ZEBRA. (5)

14 .... is to IN as EXIT is to OUT. (8)

17 .... is to ORANGE as SHELL is to NUT. (4)

19 VICTORY is to DEFEAT as .... is to FAILURE. (7)

22 MUTTON is to SHEEP as .... is to CALF. (4)

23 .... is to HOUSE as FUNNEL is to SHIP. (7)

Down ↓

1 .... is to GROOM as WIFE is to HUSBAND. (5)

3 FOOD is to HUNGER as DRINK is to .... (6)

4 NIECE is to .... as AUNT is to UNCLE. (6)

5 FIN is to FISH as WING is to .... (4)

8 MOUTH is to PERSON as .... is to BIRD. (4)

9 .... is to ARM as KNEE is to LEG. (5)

10 .... is to NEIGH as PIG is to GRUNT. (5)

11 OPTICIAN is to EYES as CHIROPODIST is to .... (4)

13 DAY is to NIGHT as .... is to DUSK. (4)

15 NOSE is to SMELL as TONGUE is to .... (5)

16 TEN is to DECADE as HUNDRED is to .... (7)

18 TURKEY is to CHRISTMAS as .... is to EASTER. (3)

20 PLATE is to CROCKERY as SPOON is to .... (7)

21 CUFF is to ARM as .... is to NECK. (6)

15 'St-' words

Complete the following crossword. Each word begins with the letters 'st-'.

Across →

2 Glue is this. So is jam. (6)

3 The sports ground where football, baseball, etc. is played. (7)

4 Not bent or twisted. (8)

7 If your mother married again, her husband would be your .... (10)

9   You might have to use these if the lift is out of order. (6)

10   To look at someone or something for a long time. (5)

11   A small, narrow river. (6)

12   Something women wear on their legs. (9)

14   The right side of a ship (when you are facing towards the front). (9)

17   To take something that is not legally yours. (5)

18   When we visited New York we went to see the .... of Liberty. (6)

19   Workers often do this to try to get better pay or working conditions. (6)

20   A man whose job it is to do all the dangerous things in a film for the actors. (8)

22   Of bread or cakes, not fresh. (5)

23   Part of a car. You use this when you want to turn left or right. (8,5)

Down ↓

1   Very bad weather, with heavy rain, strong winds and often thunder and lightning. (5)

3   A state of worry and tension caused by the problems of living, too much work, etc. (6)

5   When people do this, they suffer and sometimes die from great hunger. (6)

6   Water turns into this when it boils. (5)

7   If a hill is this, you might have to get off your bike and walk up it instead. (5)

8   A doctor uses this to listen to a patient's heart and breathing. (11)

10   The place where people buy and sell shares. (5,8)

11   A type of seat without support for your back or arms. (5)

13   Someone you have never met before. (8)

14   The raised platform in a theatre. (5)

15   A bee might do this if it was being attacked or was trying to protect its hive. (5)

16   The place where an artist works. (6)

19   If you have this, you find it difficult to say the first sound of a word and so you often hesitate or say it two or three times e.g. *I c-c-can't come tonight.* (Another word for 'stammer'.) (7)

20   A building in which horses are kept. (6)

21   To walk in a slow, relaxed way, usually for pleasure. (6)

Picture crossword: in the kitchen

Look at the drawings and complete the crosword. Some are two-word answers.

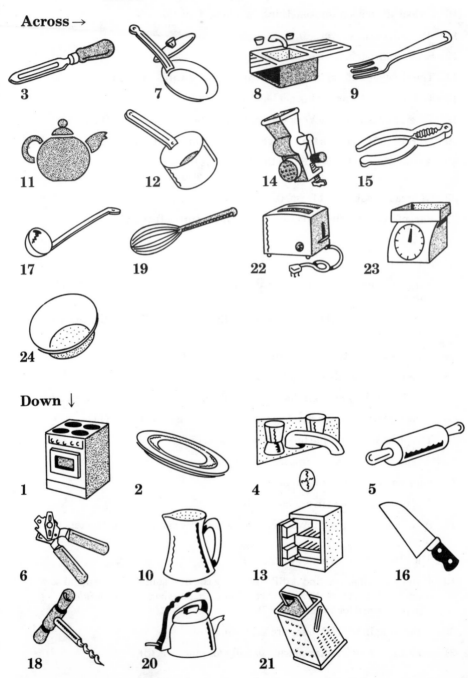

Across →

3 7 8 9

11 12 14 15

17 19 22 23

24

Down ↓

1 2 4 5

6 10 13 16

18 20 21

Parts of the body

Put the mixed-up letters for each word in the right order to complete the crossword. Each word is a part of the body. To help you, the answers are given in alphabetical order at the foot of page 39.

Across →		**Down** ↓	
3	alnek (5)	1	celuknk (7)
6	inch (4)	2	enke (4)
7	blowe (5)	4	yorbewe (7)
8	lehe (4)	5	tofo (4)
10	seno (4)	8	deha (4)
11	rehfdoae (8)	9	ptleem (6)
16	toirnls (7)	12	ounteg (6)
18	gel (3)	13	mapl (4)
19	deeliy (6)	14	mar (3)
23	saer (4) (*plural*)	15	seye (4) (*plural*)
24	ledsohru (8)	17	erignf (6)
25	ote (3)	20	tesch (5)
26	stiwa (5)	21	touhm (5)
27	hartot (6)	22	awj (3)
28	mubht (5)	24	cotahsm (7)
31	hecke (5)	29	pih (3)
32	nahd (4)	30	syleeah (7)
33	hight (5)		

ankle   arm   cheek   chest   chin   ears   elbow   eyebrow
eyelash   eyelid   eyes   finger   foot   forehead   hand   head
heel   hip   jaw   knee   knuckle   leg   mouth   nose   nostril
palm   shoulder   stomach   temple   thigh   throat   thumb   toe
tongue   waist

18 Synonyms

Complete the crossword by finding a synonym for each of the adjectives, verbs and nouns on page 41.

Across →		Down ↓	
2	awful (8)	**1**	leave (6)
6	mend (6)	**3**	wicked (4)
7	error (7)	**4**	happy (4)
8	sadness (6)	**5**	freedom (7)
10	expensive (4)	**6**	need (v) (7)
11	impolite (4)	**8**	peculiar (7)
12	prison (4)	**9**	anxiety (5)
13	weep (3)	**14**	alter (6)
14	competition (7)	**15**	completely quiet (6)
16	very big (8)	**17**	swim (v) (5)
20	help (n) (10)	**18**	present (n) (4)
21	detest (4)	**19**	good-looking (8)
23	go in (5)	**21**	occur (6)
25	odour (5)	**22**	employment (4)
26	sad (7)	**24**	attempt (v) (3)

Word association 2

Complete the crossword by finding out which word each of the groups of three words can be associated with.

Across →

1   hail, sleet, forecast (7)

5   lace, heel, sole (4)

6   river, rod, trout (7)

7   beer, barman, pint (3)

9   pilot, seat belt, wings (9)

10 tweed, lapel, sleeves (6)

12 aisle, Sunday, pulpit (6)

16 diamonds, bridge, shuffle (5)

17 horoscope, Gemini, zodiac (9)

20 helmet, uniform, truncheon (9)

Down ↓

2   compartment, engine, platform (5)

3   capital, Thames, Big Ben (6)

4   keyboard, disk, mouse (8)

8   conductor, symphony, percussion (9)

11 bishop, pawn, checkmate (5)

13 claws, purr, siamese (3)

14 cot, pram, nappy (4)

15 cover, chapter, title (4)

18 deck, anchor, cruise (4)

19 vault, account, loan (4)

Mixed up clues 2

In this crossword, all the words have been filled in, but the clues are all mixed up. Write the correct answer (1 Down, 8 Across, etc.) in front of each clue.

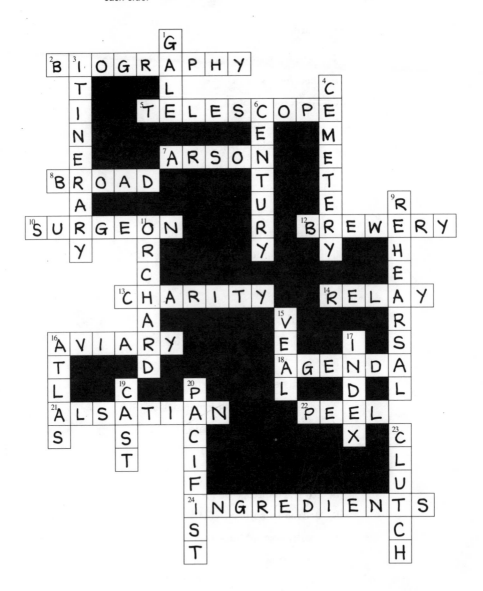

.... All the actors in a play or film.

.... A written account of someone's life.

.... The place where beer is made.

.... A plan of a journey which includes the names of places to be seen and visited.

.... The skin of an orange, apple, etc.

.... A period of a hundred years.

.... A field of fruit trees.

.... A large enclosure or cage for keeping birds in.

.... A person who believes all forms of war to be wrong.

.... An occasion in which actors practise and learn their speeches etc. before performing in public.

.... An instrument to make distant objects, e.g. stars, look bigger.

.... The list of items to be discussed at a meeting.

.... A very strong wind.

.... A synonym for 'wide'.

.... A large wolf-like dog often used by the police or for guarding property.

.... A book of maps.

.... A doctor who performs operations at a hospital.

.... The list of different foods needed to cook a dish.

.... The meat we get from a calf.

.... A place where dead people are buried.

.... The crime of setting fire to houses, shops, etc. often for the insurance money.

.... A society or organization that gives help in the form of gifts, clothing or money to the poor.

.... A table of reference, usually at the back of a book, where key words are listed alphabetically together with the page numbers on which they occur.

.... An athletics event in which teams of four people take part. Each person only runs part of the distance.

.... The pedal in a car which you press before you change gear.

21 6-letter words

In this crossword, each of the missing words has six letters. The first and last letter of each word is given, with a clue.

Across →

2 N_ _ _ _W A relative.

4 G_ _ _ _E To look quickly at something.

6 M_ _ _ _L A book of instructions e.g. for a car, computer program, etc.

8 F_ _ _ _T A large area of land covered with trees.

11 S_ _ _ _M A loud cry.

12 P_ _ _ _N People who break the law may be sent here.

13 L_ _ _T e.g. bee, beetle, spider.

15 S_ _ _ _B An outer area of a town or city where people live.

17 M_ _ _ _E Fully developed or ripe fruit, wine, cheese, etc.

18 B_ _ _ _H Part of a tree.

19 P_ _ _ _C An outdoor meal, e.g. in the country, using food that you have brought with you.

24 R_ _ _ _E A list of ingredients and a set of instructions that tells you how to cook something.

25 C_ _ _ _O A building or a room where you can play cards or other games, e.g. roulette, for money.

26 B_ _ _ _E A light, gentle wind.

29 M_ _ _ _R To deliberately kill a person.

32 R_ _ _ _E To save or set someone free from danger or harm.

33 C_ _ _ _D Someone who is easily afraid; not at all brave.

34 S_ _ _ _E A shape of four equal sides.

35 S_ _ _ _Y The money you are paid each month for your job.

Down ↓

1 P_ _ _ _E A very important word in English if you want to be polite.

3 P_ _ _ _R A large notice, picture or photograph that you put up on a wall or noticeboard, often to advertise something.

5 F_ _ _ _D The opposite of 'allow'.

7 L_ _ _S The words of a song.

8 F_ _ _ _S Very well-known.

9 V_ _ _ _N A musical instrument.

10 R_ _ _ _T To do or say something again.

14 N_ _ _ _Y A country in Europe.

16 R_ _ _ _E To stop working, usually because you have reached a certain age.

20 I_ _ _ _D A piece of land surrounded by water.

21 S_ _ _ _E People with colds do this a lot.

22 K_ _ _N A young cat.

23 A_ _ _ _D To go up.

27 R_ _ _ _Y The part of an airport where planes take off and land.

28 C_ _ _ _E A holiday on a ship.

30 P_ _ _ _L Your car wouldn't get very far without this.

31 P_ _ _ _T What every company hopes to make. (The opposite of 'loss'.)

Complete the crossword by filling in the missing words in the sentences.
To help you, the first letter of each word is given.

Across →

1 I don't know him all that well, really. He's just an a.................... (12)

7 Twenty people work for Mrs Slater. She has twenty e.................... (9)

8 Most of the people who rented the flats were immigrants. In fact, most of the t.................... came from India. (7)

11 George works for his cousin, Arthur. Arthur is George's e.................... (8)

12 My sister's husband has just been put in charge of the local newspaper. He's the new e.................... (6)

14 We rent our flat from Mr Parker. He is our l.................... (8)

16 Thirteen people died in the plane crash. Among the v.................... were five schoolchildren. (7)

18 Mark and Deborah own the business together. Deborah is Mark's p.................... (7)

20 She was the only one who was not killed in the crash. She was the only s.................... (8)

21 David Wilson has been my solicitor for over forty years. I am one of his oldest c.................... (7)

22 David takes the place of the boss when she's away. He's her d.................... (6)

Down ↓

2 Karen is my Uncle Bob's daughter. She's my c.................... (6)

3 My brother was born on the same day as me. He is my t.................... (4)

4 'May I introduce my c...................., Charles White. He works in the sales department and I'm in the accounts department.' (9)

5 Mr Jones buys his goods at my shop. He's a c.................... of mine. (8)

6 He's always hitting smaller or weaker boys. He's such a b.................... (5)

9 Timothy and Barbara have been going out with each other for almost nine months. It's the longest time Barbara has had the same b.................... (9)

10 Mrs Brown's husband died three years ago. She has been a w.................... for three years. (5)

13 I go to Mr Tomkins to have my hair cut. He's been my b.................... since I was a boy. (6)

15 Samantha and Simon have just got engaged. Samantha is Simon's f.................... (7)

17 Mrs Grove makes all Pamela's dresses. She is her d.................... (10)

18 People usually call for Mr Sanders when they want to fit a new bath or a shower. He's the best p.................... in the area. (7)

19 Neither of her parents is alive. She's an o.................... (6)

23 Three jokes

Complete the crossword by filling in the missing words in the three jokes.
To help you, the first letter of each word is given.

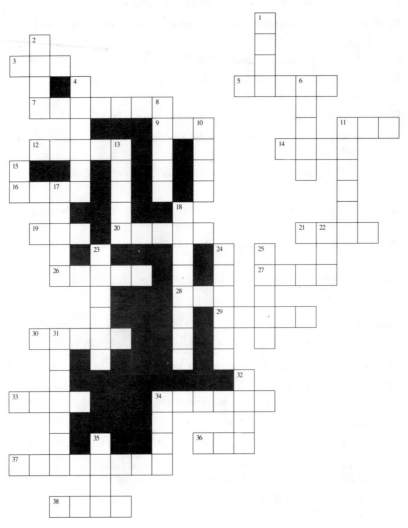

Joke 1

A farmer's wife was expecting a b....................(27 across) and the town doctor was
called out in the m....................(4 down) of the night to the farmhouse. It was miles
away from a....................(18 down) and was extremely old-fashioned. In
f....................(34 down), it didn't even have electricity.

The doctor went to the farmer's wife and the nervous farmer w....................(19
across) called to assist. He stood holding the oil lamp in o....................(12 across) to
give the doctor light.

'Hold the lamp closer,' s....................(33 across) the doctor, and within minutes a
boy was b....................(32 down)

'Hang on a minute!' said the doctor. 'I think you're g....................(8 down) to have twins. Bring the lamp closer.'

Five minutes l.....................(30 across) a twin baby girl came into the world. The farmer was still recovering f...................(35 down) the shock when the doctor called out, 'Hold on a minute. I do believe you're going to have triplets. C...................(38 across) closer with the lamp.'

And soon, another baby appeared. The farmer sat down in a c...................(6 down), white-faced.

'Good heavens!' said the doctor. 'I t...................(20 across) it could be quads. Come closer and h...................(2 down) the lamp.'

'Not likely!' said the farmer. 'I'm not that stupid. It's the blasted light w...................(5 across) keeps attracting them!'

Joke 2

Judith was talking to h...................(28 across) friend, Jenny.

'Joey gave me s...................(1 down) a shock yesterday.'

'Joey? You mean your budgerigar?'

'Yes, poor little thing. I'd just f...................(23 down) up my lighter with petrol before letting him out of his cage for his exercise. I hadn't noticed that I'd spilled s...................(16 across) of it on the table. Well, Joey noticed it of course and b...................(11 down) I could stop him he'd flown onto the table and taken two or three beakfuls.'

'What happened?'

'Well, he gave a very loud squawk, flew straight up and hit the ceiling. Then he flew three times r...................(29 across) the room, going faster and faster all the t................... .'(10 down)

'Good heavens!'

'Then he flew o...................(9 across) into the hall, into the kitchen, out of the kitchen back into the hall again, and finally into the bathroom. There he f...................(21 across) straight at the mirror and smacked his little head a...................(31 down) the glass and then fell into the washbasin. And there he l...................(22 down) on his back not moving.'

'What? You mean he was dead?'

'No, he'd just r...................(36 across) out of petrol!'

Joke 3

A motorist was d...................(7 across) through the country when he stopped f...................(3 across) a hitch-hiker. The hitch-hiker was holding a cow.

'I can g...................(14 across) you a lift,' said the motorist, 'b...................(11 across) I can't take your cow'.

'Oh, don't worry,' said the hitch-hiker, 'she'll f...................(34 across) us in her own time'.

So the hitch-hiker got in and the m...................(37 across) started up. He drove at 50 kilometres an hour and the cow ran along behind him. He drove at 60 kilometres an hour and the cow was s...................(26 across) running behind him. He drove at 70 kilometres an hour, yet the cow was somehow managing to keep up with him. But he noticed in his m...................(24 down) that the cow seemed to be tiring a...................(15 down) her tongue was hanging out of her mouth.

'I'm worried a...................(25 down) your cow,' said the motorist to his passenger. 'Her tongue is hanging out of the right side of her mouth.'

'Oh, that's all r................... ,'(13 down) said the hitch-hiker, 'it just m...................(17 down) she's going to overtake!'

24 British and American English

The words in italics in the sentences are American English. Complete the crossword by writing down the British words for them. To help you, the answers are given but the letters are mixed up. (See example)

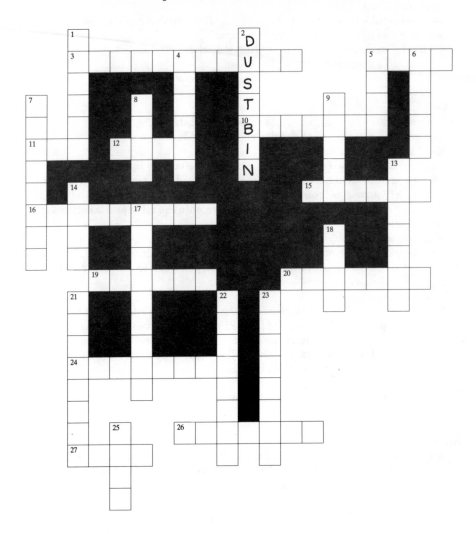

Across →

3 The best way of getting about in New York is by *subway* (GURORNDDUNE) (11)

5 Do you feel like going to see a *movie* tonight? (LIMF) (4)

10 Would you like a *cookie* with your coffee? (TUISBIC) (7)

11 There's a *can* of tomato soup if you're hungry. (NIT) (3)

12 He took out a hundred dollar *bill* and gave it to the saleswoman. (TONE) (4)

15 We're driving to France in the summer. Do you know how much *gasoline* costs over there? (TOLERP) (6)

16 I can't decide whether to wear a *vest* with my suit or not. (CASIATWOT) (9)

19 'If you're good,' said the baby-sitter to the small child, 'I'll let you have some *candy* later on.' (SEESTW) (6)

20 I'm afraid Ms Collins is on *vacation* this week. Is there anyone else you could speak to? (AOYLIDH) (7)

24 The mother told her young child to get off the road and walk on the *sidewalk*. (TEEPVAMN) (8)

26 'Have you remembered your credit card, Doris?'
'Yes, it's in my *purse*.' (BANGDAH) (7)

27 A *streetcar* is far better for the environment than a bus – especially diesel buses. (RAMT) (4)

Down →

1 Our German course doesn't start until the *fall*. (TANMUU) (6)

2 Throw this broken vase into the *trashcan*. (SINBUDT) (7)

4 'Where are the children?'
'They're playing outside in the *yard*, I think.' (RENGAD) (6)

5 How much do you pay each month for your *apartment*? (LAFT) (4)

6 When I was a child I always wanted to be a *truck* driver. (RORYL) (5)

7 There was a terrible accident on the *freeway* this morning. (ROOTWMAY) (8)

8 What happened to that small *store* at the corner of Fourth Avenue? (HOPS) (4)

9 In Britain you are expected to *stand in line* for a bus. (EQEUU) (5)

13 'Has the *mailman* been yet?'
'Yes, but there was nothing for you, I'm afraid.' (SNOTAMP) (7)

14 We'll have to use to stairs; the *elevator* is out of order. (FILT) (4)

17 Have you seen the *janitor*? I think there's something wrong with my radiator. (CATKERREA) (9)

18 'Waiter, could I have the *check*, please?' (LIBL) (4)

21 She wasn't looking where she was going and bumped into a *streetlight*. (SMAPLOPT) (8)

22 I need some new *drapes* for the bedroom window. (CRINASUT) (8)

23 'Have you seen my green skirt, John?'
'It's in your *closet*, I think.' (BRERADOW) (8)

25 We can play poker if someone has a *deck* of cards. (CAPK) (4)

Word-building

The word in CAPITALS at the end of each of the sentences can be used to form a word that fits the gap. Use these words to complete the crossword. (See example)

Across →

2 I don't really think there is a .... to the problem; at least not in the near future. (8) **SOLVE**

3 It's .... arguing with her. She never listens to what you say. (7) **USE**

4 We could hear a dog barking .... from inside the house as we knocked on the front door. (7) **ANGRY**

7 Do you want to go to the pub or the cinema tonight? You decide. It's your .... (6) **CHOOSE**

9 The accident was due to the bus driver's .... (12) **CARE**

11 What is the .... of the river at this point? (5) **DEEP**

12 Don't talk about your operation in front of Paul. You know how .... he is about his health. (9) **SENSE**

14 I want .... of your love. Lend me £100! (5) **PROVE**

15 Oh, grow up, David! Stop being so ....! (8) **CHILD**

19 Although more and more British people now own their own homes, there is also an increasing number of families who are .... (8) **HOME**

20 She takes a lot of .... in her work (5) **PROUD**

22 If you're going to the supermarket, don't forget to get a packet of .... peas. (6) **FREEZE**

23 I'm sorry, I .... with you completely. I don't think men and women can ever be equal. (8) **AGREE**

Down ↓

1 The .... of the Scottish Highlands is hard to describe in words. It has to be experienced at first-hand. (6) **BEAUTIFUL**

2 There is a .... of teachers in London and other major cities. (8) **SHORT**

3 If you ask me, guns are very .... toys for children. (10) **SUIT**

5 I'm not saying he doesn't have the .... to do the job. All I'm worried about is whether he'll fit into the team or not. (7) **ABLE**

6 To everyone's surprise the company made a .... of several million pounds. (4) **LOSE**

8 Who can tell me the .... of the Eiffel Tower? (6) **HIGH**

10 Most people feel nervous if they have to make a .... in public. (6) **SPEAK**

13 You need both skill and .... to be a ballet dancer. (8) **STRONG**

16 Have they reached a .... yet? (8) **DECIDE**

17 Their attempt to climb Mount Everest ended in .... (7) **FAIL**

18 It has been a .... to do business with you. (8) **PLEASE**

21 I found the recipe in a Scandinavian .... book. (7) **COOK**

Answers

1 Opposites: adjectives

Across
2 present   4 alive   6 tight   9 shallow   11 careless   12 sharp
16 smooth   17 untidy   18 useless   20 tame   22 fresh
23 positive
Down
1 professional   3 even   5 light   7 incorrect   8 sober
10 generous   13 permanent   14 public   15 noisy   19 narrow
21 awake

2 Picture crossword: fruit and vegetables

Across
1 cauliflower   5 cabbage   8 grapes   9 peach   10 peas   11 onion
13 prunes   14 plum   15 beetroot   16 celery   17 lettuce
20 orange   21 avocado   22 gooseberry
Down
1 cucumber   2 leek   3 rhubarb   4 grapefruit   6 blackberry
7 mushrooms   9 pineapple   12 asparagus   16 cherry   18 tomato
19 lemon

3 Complete the sentences

Across
3 knife   5 receipt   9 postage   11 post office   12 deaf   13 salary
15 Bless   16 scissors   17 pet   20 umbrella   22 headline
24 library   25 view
Down
1 dictionary   2 fit   4 diet   6 chimney   7 goals   8 milk
9 petrol   10 alphabetical   14 glasses   17 platform   18 questions
19 chemist   21 airport   23 lift

4 Jobs and occupations

Across
3 traffic warden   4 architect   7 doctor   9 nurse   12 dentist
13 hairdresser   16 farmer   19 secretary   20 miner   23 butcher
26 vet   28 pilot   29 estate agent   30 optician
Down
1 waitress   2 teacher   5 carpenter   6 journalist   8 dustman
10 salesman   11 librarian   14 baker   15 businessman
17 electrician   18 actor   21 chef   22 policeman   24 mechanic
25 barber   27 postman

5 Classifications

Across

1 languages	5 jewellery	6 crimes	8 vegetables	9 dates
12 cutlery	13 trees	15 shapes	16 continents	17 fruit
18 vehicles	19 planets	20 reptiles		

Down

2 animals   3 games   4 metals   7 weights   10 currencies
11 weapons   14 insects

6 People 1

Across

3 shoplifter   6 ambassador   10 vegetarian   13 spy
15 murderer   18 witness   19 architect   20 traitor

Down

1 thief   2 optimist   4 refugee   5 jockey   7 burglar
8 pedestrian   9 bachelor   11 tourist   12 composer   14 opponent
16 newsagent   17 spectator

7 Collective nouns

Across

4 dozen   5 pint   6 tube   8 pairs   10 note   11 packet   12 ball
14 piece   16 crowd

Down

1 chest   2 bottle   3 pile   5 pane   7 bunch   8 pot   9 roll
11 pack   12 bar   13 loaf   14 pound   15 box

8 Picture crossword: animals

Across

2 beetle   4 owl   6 lobster   8 mouse   10 donkey   12 crab
14 duck   16 eagle   18 pig   20 bat   21 tortoise   22 snail
23 rabbit   24 goose

Down

1 frog   2 bull   3 worm   5 squirrel   7 snake   9 hedgehog
11 octopus   13 butterfly   15 cow   17 goat   19 fox   22 spider

9 Opposites: verbs

Across

1 attack   2 disappear   4 raise   6 shorten   7 tighten   10 create
11 refuse   12 expand   14 spend   15 depart   16 allow   18 forget
19 decrease

Down

1 admit   3 show   5 sink   6 succeed   8 import   9 hurry
13 discourage   14 strengthen   17 reward

10 Word association 1

Across
4 hospital   6 dog   8 tree   10 library   12 flower   13 Christmas
14 painting   17 bicycle   18 car   19 river   20 shirt   22 tennis
Down
1 football   2 bird   3 astronomy   5 bed   7 golf   9 newspaper
11 athletics   15 telephone   16 school   21 wedding

11 Mixed up clues 1

3 Down	A person who pays to stay ...
6 Down	A type of fish.
5 Across	A common illness ...
12 Down	A religious festival ...
2 Across	Unable to read or write.
7 Across	Used to stick things together ...
4 Down	The main part of a tree.
9 Down	The yellow part of an egg.
19 Across	To travel regularly a long distance ...
18 Down	Part of a car ...
13 Across	A natural disaster ...
22 Across	A container for money.
1 Down	To walk unsteadily ...
20 Across	One of the signs of the zodiac ...
11 Down	Being able to speak two languages ...
21 Down	A common yellow spring flower.
8 Across	To look quickly at something.
16 Down	Very old.
10 Down	Expecting a baby.
24 Across	How some people feel ...
15 Across	To talk about other people ...
23 Down	A word that ends with the same sound ...
11 Across	Having no money.
17 Across	The line running from the front ...
14 Down	Your voice may sound like this ...

12 The dinner party

Across
3 neighbour   5 while   6 dinner   9 mine   10 meal   14 away
15 make   16 closing   18 them   21 found   23 onto   24 Just
26 could   28 heard   29 rest   30 explain
Down
1 whether   2 her   3 not   4 rung   5 worked   7 finished
8 pleased   11 cat   12 left   13 same   14 again   16 couple
17 sorry   19 must   20 nobody   22 noticed   25 success
26 called   27 thanked

13 One word only

Across

2 neighbours   5 niece   8 crew   9 exit   11 apologised/apologized
14 escalators   15 audience   17 famine   18 arrested   20 gradually

Down

1 shrink   3 emigrate   4 fortnight   6 escape   7 applicants
10 improved   12 decided   13 voluntary   16 refused   19 decade

14 EYE is to SEE as EAR is to HEAR

Across

2 directory   5 bee   6 trunk   7 hear   8 butcher   11 flock
12 spots   14 entrance   17 peel   19 success   22 veal
23 chimney

Down

1 bride   3 thirst   4 nephew   5 bird   8 beak   9 elbow
10 horse   11 feet   13 dawn   15 taste   16 century   18 egg
20 cutlery   21 collar

15 'St-' words

Across

2 sticky   3 stadium   4 straight   7 stepfather   9 stairs   10 stare
11 stream   12 stockings   14 starboard   17 steal   18 statue
19 strike   20 stuntman   22 stale   23 steering wheel

Down

1 storm   3 stress   5 starve   6 steam   7 steep   8 stethoscope
10 Stock Exchange   11 stool   13 stranger   14 stage   15 sting
16 studio   19 stutter   20 stable   21 stroll

16 Picture crosswords: in the kitchen

Across

3 potato peeler   7 frying pan   8 sink   9 fork   11 teapot
12 saucepan   14 mincer   15 nutcracker   17 ladle   19 whisk
22 toaster   23 scales   24 bowl

Down

1 cooker   2 plate   4 tap   5 rolling pin   6 tin opener   10 jug
13 fridge   16 knife   18 corkscrew   20 kettle   21 grater

17 Parts of the body

Across

3 ankle   6 chin   7 elbow   8 heel   10 nose   11 forehead
16 nostril   18 leg   19 eyelid   23 ears   24 shoulder   25 toe
26 waist   27 throat   28 thumb   31 cheek   32 hand   33 thigh

Down

1 knuckle   2 knee   4 eyebrow   5 foot   8 head   9 temple
12 tongue   13 palm   14 arm   15 eyes   17 finger   20 chest
21 mouth   22 jaw   24 stomach   29 hip   30 eyelash

18 Synonyms

Across
2 terrible   6 repair   7 mistake   8 sorrow   10 dear   11 rude
12 jail/gaol   13 cry   14 contest   16 enormous   20 assistance
21 hate   23 enter   25 smell   26 unhappy
Down
1 depart   3 evil   4 glad   5 liberty   6 require   8 strange
9 worry   14 change   15 silent   17 bathe   18 gift   19 handsome
21 happen   22 work   24 try

19 Word association 2

Across
1 weather   5 shoe   6 fishing   7 pub   9 aeroplane   10 jacket
12 church   16 cards   17 astrology   20 policeman
Down
2 train   3 London   4 computer   8 orchestra   11 chess   13 cat
14 baby   15 book   18 ship   19 bank

20 Mixed up clues 2

19 Down   All the actors in a play or film.
2 Across   A written account of someone's life.
12 Across   The place where beer is made.
3 Down   A plan of a journey …
22 Across   The skin of an orange, apple, etc.
6 Down   A period of a hundred years.
11 Down   A field of fruit trees.
16 Across   A large enclosure or cage …
20 Down   A person who believes all forms …
9 Down   An occasion when actors practise …
5 Across   An instrument to make distant …
18 Across   The list of items to be discussed …
1 Down   A very strong wind.
8 Across   A synonym for 'wide'.
21 Across   A large wolf-like dog …
16 Down   A book of maps.
10 Across   A doctor who performs operations …
24 Across   The list of different foods …
15 Down   The meat we get from a calf.
4 Down   A place where dead people are buried.
7 Across   The crime of setting fire to houses …
13 Across   A society or organization …
17 Down   A table of reference …
14 Across   An athletics event …
23 Down   The pedal in a car which you press …

21 6-letter words

Across
2 nephew   4 glance   6 manual   8 forest   11 scream   12 prison
13 insect   15 suburb   17 mature   18 branch   19 picnic

24 recipe   25 casino   26 breeze   29 murder   32 rescue
33 coward   34 square   35 salary
Down
1 please   3 poster   5 forbid   7 lyrics   8 famous   9 violin
10 repeat   14 Norway   16 retire   20 island   21 sneeze
22 kitten   23 ascend   27 runway   28 cruise   30 petrol
31 profit

22 People 2

Across
1 acquaintance   7 employees   8 tenants   11 employer   12 editor
14 landlord   16 victims   18 partner   20 survivor   21 clients
22 deputy
Down
2 cousin   3 twin   4 colleague   5 customer   6 bully   9 boyfriend
10 widow   13 barber   15 fiancée   17 dressmaker   18 plumber
19 orphan

23 Three jokes

Across
3 for   5 which   7 driving   9 out   11 but   12 order   14 give
16 some   19 was   20 think   21 flew   26 still   27 baby
28 her   29 round   30 later   33 said   34 follow   36 run
37 motorist   38 Come
Down
1 such   2 hold   4 middle   6 chair   8 going   10 time
11 before   13 right   15 as   17 means   18 anywhere   22 lay
23 filled   24 mirror   25 about   31 against   32 born   34 fact
35 from

24 British and American English

Across
3 underground   5 film   10 biscuit   11 tin   12 note   15 petrol
16 waistcoat   19 sweets   20 holiday   24 pavement   26 handbag
27 tram
Down
1 autumn   2 dustbin   4 garden   5 flat   6 lorry   7 motorway
8 shop   9 queue   13 postman   14 lift   17 caretaker   18 bill
21 lamppost   22 curtains   23 wardrobe   25 pack

25 Word-building

Across
2 solution   3 useless   4 angrily   7 choice   9 carelessness
11 depth   12 sensitive   14 proof   15 childish   19 homeless
20 pride   22 frozen   23 disagree
Down
1 beauty   2 shortage   3 unsuitable   5 ability   6 loss   8 height
10 speech   13 strength   16 decision   17 failure   18 pleasure
21 cookery

Key words

The number after each word is the crossword in which the word first appears.
(*v*=verb, *n*=noun, *a*=adjective)

ability 25
about 23
acquaintance 22
actor 4
admit 9
aeroplane 19
again 12
against 23
agenda 20
airport 3
alive 1
allow 9
alphabetical 3
alsatian 20
ambassador 6
ancient 11
angrily 25
animals 5
ankle 17
anywhere 23
apologised/
  apologized 13
applicants 13
architect 4
arm 17
arrested 13
arson 20
as 23
ascend 21
asparagus 2
assistance 18
astrology 19
astronomy 10
athletics 10
atlas 20
attack (v) 9
audience 13
autumn 24
avalanche 11
aviary 20
avocado 2
awake 1
away 12

baby 19
bachelor 6
baker 4
ball 7
bank 19
bar 7

barber 4
bat 8
bathe 18
beak 14
beauty 25
bed 10
bee 14
beetle 8
beetroot 2
before 23
bicycle 10
bilingual 11
bill 24
biography 20
bird 10
biscuit 24
blackberry 2
bless (you) 3
bonnet 11
book (n) 19
born 23
bottle 7
bowl 16
box 7
boyfriend 22
branch 21
breeze 21
brewery 20
bride 14
broad 20
broke (a) 11
bull 8
bully 22
bunch 7
burglar 6
businessman 4
but 23
butcher 4
butterfly 8

cabbage 2
called
  (=phoned) 12
Cancer 11
car 10
cards 19
careless 1
carelessness 25
caretaker 24
carpenter 4

casino 21
cast (n) 20
cat 12
cauliflower 2
celery 2
cemetery 20
century 14
chair 23
change (v) 18
charity 20
cheek 17
chef 4
chemist 3
cherry 2
chess 19
chest (of
  drawers) 7
chest (body) 17
childish 25
chimney 3
chin 17
choice 25
Christmas 10
church 19
clients 22
closing 12
clutch (n) 20
collar 13
colleague 22
come 23
commute 11
composer 6
computer 19
contest 18
continents 5
cooker 16
cookery 25
corkscrew 16
could 12
couple 12
cousin 22
cow 8
coward 21
crab 8
create 9
crew 13
crimes 5
crowd 7
cruise 21
cry (v) 18

cucumber 2
currencies 5
curtains 24
customer 22
cutlery 5

daffodil 11
dates 5
dawn 14
deaf 3
dear 18
decade 13
decided 13
decision 25
decrease 9
dentist 4
depart 9
depth 25
deputy 22
dictionary 3
diet 3
dinner 12
directory 14
disagree 25
disappear 9
discourage 9
doctor 4
dog 10
donkey 8
dozen 7
dressmaker 22
driving 23
duck (n) 8
dustbin 24
dustman 4

eagle 8
ears 17
Easter 11
editor 22
egg 14
elbow 14
electrician 4
emigrate 13
employees 22
employer 22
enormous 18
enter 18
entrance 14
escalators 13

escape (v) 13
estate agent 4
even 1
evil 18
exit 13
expand 9
explain 12
eyebrow 17
eyelash 17
eyelid 17
eyes 17

fact 23
failure 25
famine 13
famous 21
farmer 4
feet 14
fiancée 22
filled 23
film (n) 24
finger 17
finished 12
fishing 19
fit (v) 3
flat (n) 24
flew 23
flock 14
flower 10
follow 23
foot 17
football 10
for 23
forbid 21
forehead 17
forest 21
forget 9
fork 16
fortnight 13
found 12
fox 8
fresh 1
fridge 16
frog 8
from 23
frozen 25
fruit 5
frying pan 16

gale 20
games 5
gaol 18
garden 24
generous 1
giddy 11
gift 18

give 23
glad 18
glance (v) 11
glasses
  (=spectacles) 3
glue 11
goals 3
goat 8
going 23
golf 10
goose 8
gooseberry 2
gossip (v) 11
gradually 13
grapefruit 2
grapes 2
grater 16

hairdresser 4
hand 17
handbag 24
handsome 18
happen 18
hate (v) 18
head 17
headline 3
hear 14
heard 12
hedgehog 8
heel 17
height 25
her 12
hip 17
hoarse 11
hold 23
holiday 24
homeless 25
horse 14
hospital 10
hurry (v) 9

illiterate 11
import (v) 9
improved 13
incorrect 1
index 20
ingredients 20
insect 21
insects 5
island 21
itinerary 20

jacket 19
jail 18
jaw 17
jewellery 5

jockey 6
journalist 4
jug 16
just 12

kettle 16
kitten 21
knee 17
knife 3
knuckle 17

ladle 16
lamppost 24
landlord 22
languages 5
later 23
lay 23
leek 2
left (v) 12
leg 17
lemon 2
lettuce 2
liberty 18
librarian 4
library 3
lift (n) 3
light (a) 1
loaf 7
lobster 8
lodger 11
London 19
lorry 24
loss 25
lyrics 21

make 12
manual (n) 21
mature (a) 21
meal 12
means (v) 23
mechanic 4
metals 5
middle 23
milk 3
mincer 16
mine 12
miner 4
mirror 23
mistake 18
motorist 23
motorway 24
mouse 8
mouth 17
mumps 11
murder (v) 21
murderer 6

mushrooms 2
must 12

narrow 1
neighbour 12
neighbours 13
nephew 14
newsagent 6
newspaper 10
niece 13
nobody 12
noisy 1
Norway 21
nose 17
nostril 17
not 12
note (money) 7
noticed 12
nurse 4
nutcracker 16

octopus 8
onion 2
onto 12
opponent 6
optician 4
optimist 6
orange (n) 2
orchard 20
orchestra 19
order (in ... to) 23
orphan 22
out 23
owl 8

pacifist 20
pack (n) 7
packet 7
painting 10
pairs 7
palm 17
pane 7
parting 11
partner 22
pavement 24
peach 2
peas 2
pedestrian 6
peel (n) 14
permanent 1
pet 3
petrol 3
picnic 21
piece 7
pig 8
pile 7

pilot 4
pineapple 2
pint 7
plaice 11
planets 5
plate 16
platform 3
please 21
pleased 12
pleasure 25
plum 2
plumber 22
policeman 4
positive 1
post office 3
postage 3
poster 21
postman 4
pot 7
potato peeler 16
pound 7
pregnant 11
present (a) 1
pride 25
prison 21
professional 1
profit 21
proof 25
prunes 2
pub 19
public (a) 1

questions 3
queue (v) 24

rabbit 8
raise 9
receipt 3
recipe 21
refugee 6
refuse (v) 9
refused 13
rehearsal 20
relay 20
repair 18
repeat 21
reptiles 5
require 18
rescue (v) 21
rest (n) 12
retire 21
reward (v) 9
rhubarb 2
rhyme (n) 11
right (direction) 23
river 10
roll (n) 7
rolling pin 16

round 23
rude 18
run 23
runway 21
rung (v) 12

said 23
salary 3
salesman 4
same 12
saucepan 16
scales 16
school 10
scissors 3
scream (n) 21
secretary 4
sensitive 25
shallow 1
shapes (n) 5
sharp 1
ship 19
shirt 10
shoe 19
shop (n) 24
shoplifter 6
shortage 25
shorten 9
shoulder 17
show (v) 9
shrink 13
silent 18
sink (v) 9
sink (n) 16
smell (n) 18
smooth 1
snail 8
snake 8
sneeze 21
sober 1
solution 25
some 23
sorrow 18
sorry 12
spectator 6
speech 25
spend 9
spider 8
spots 14
spy 6
square (n) 21
squirrel 8
stable (n) 15
stadium 15
stage 15
stagger 11
stairs 15
stale 15
starboard 15

stare 15
starve 15
statue 15
steal 15
steam 15
steep 15
steering wheel 15
stepfather 15
stethoscope 15
sticky 15
still (a) 23
sting (v) 15
Stock Exchange 15
stockings 15
stomach 17
stool 15
storm 15
straight 15
strange 18
stranger 15
stream 15
strength 25
strengthen 9
stress (n) 15
strike (v) 15
stroll 15
studio 15
stuntman 15
stutter 15
suburb 21
succeed 9
success 12
such 23
surgeon 20
survivor 22
sweets 24

tame (a) 1
tap (n) 16
taste (n) 14
teacher 4
teapot 16
telephone (n) 10
telescope 20
temple 17
tenants 22
tennis 10
terrible 18
thanked 12
them 12
thief 6
thigh 17
think 23
thirst 14
throat 17
thumb 17
tight 1
tighten 9

time 23
tin 24
tin opener 16
toaster 16
toe 17
tomato 2
tongue 17
tortoise 8
tourist 6
traffic warden 4
train (n) 19
traitor 6
tram 24
tree 10
trees 5
trunk 11
try 18
tube 7
twin (n) 22

umbrella 3
underground 24
unhappy 18
unsuitable 25
untidy 1
useless 1
veal 14
vegetables 5
vegetarian 6
vehicles 5
vet 4
victims 22
view 3
vioin 21
voluntary 13

waist 17
waistcoat 24
waitress 4
wallet 11
wardrobe 24
was 23
weapons 5
weather 19
wedding 10
weights 5
whether 12
which 23
while 12
whisk (n) 16
widow 22
witness (n) 6
work (n) 18
worked 12
worm 8
worry (n) 18

yolk 11